MATHS WORD PROBLEMS GRADE 2
80+ Reading Maths Word Problems workbook for kids.

Copyright © 2019 by G. R. Griffins

Printed in the United States of America

1st Edition 2019

GM Publishing
4866 Harper Street
Paducah,KY 42003

Word Problem # 1

Read the word problem below.

Last year, 43 stores opened
for business at the outlet mall.
Due to low sales, 3 of the stores
closed down. How many stores
are open for business at the
outlet mall now?

Write the equation , Show your work and solve it.

Your Answer is . . . .

Word Problem # 2

Read the word problem below.

There are 18 chickens on the farm. 6 of the chickens are in the field and the rest are in the barn. How many chickens are in the barn?

Write the equation , Show your work and solve it.

Your Answer is . . . .

Word Problem # 3

Read the word problem below.

Mr. Celler sells colored pencils. He sells 9 green, 5 blue, and 4 yellow pencils. How many more green pencils did he sell than blue?

Write the equation , Show your work and solve it.

Your Answer is . . . .

Word Problem # 4

Read the word problem below.

Ray has 20 stickers in her collection. Leia has 15 in her collection. How many more stickers does Leia have?

Write the equation , Show your work and solve it.

Your Answer is . . . .

Word Problem # 5

Read the word problem below.

Greg makes a pattern with circles and squares. There are 12 shapes in the pattern. 8 shapes are circles. How many are squares?

Write the equation , Show your work and solve it.

Your Answer is . . . .

Word Problem # 6

Read the word problem below.

Penny has 12 apples. She gives 6 to her sister and then she eats 1. How many apples are left?

Write the equation , Show your work and solve it.

Your Answer is . . . .

Word Problem # 7

Read the word problem below.

Nine children are in line for lunch. Molly is in the middle of the line. How many children are in front of her? How many people are in back of her?

Write the equation , Show your work and solve it.

Your Answer is . . . .

Word Problem # 8

Read the word problem below.

Brown draws 2 squares and 2 triangle. How many sides does he draw in all?

Write the equation , Show your work and solve it.

Your Answer is . . . .

Word Problem # 9

Read the word problem below.

Amanda has 7 pennies. She gives 7 pennies to her brother. How many pennies does she have left?

Write the equation , Show your work and solve it.

Your Answer is . . . .

Word Problem # 10

Read the word problem below.

Greg has 7 toy cars. He gets 2 more toy cars. Maggie has 7 toy cars. Who has more toy cars?

Write the equation , Show your work and solve it.

Your Answer is . . . .

Word Problem # 11

Read the word problem below.

Jason has 8 pennies. He gets 4 more from his brother and 2 more from his sister. How many pennies does Jason have now?

Write the equation , Show your work and solve it.

Your Answer is . . . .

Word Problem # 12

Read the word problem below.

There are 13 fire trucks in the parade. 7 fire trucks have gone by. How many fire trucks will still pass by in the parade?

Write the equation , Show your work and solve it.

Your Answer is . . . .

Word Problem # 13

Read the word problem below.

Eli and his friend are in line at the movies. 5 people are in front of them. 9 people are behind. How many people are in line?

Write the equation , Show your work and solve it.

Your Answer is . . . .

Word Problem # 14

Read the word problem below.

John collects 8 stamps. Riley gives him 7 more stamps. Then John trades 7 stamps for a pencil. How many stamps does John have now?

Write the equation , Show your work and solve it.

Your Answer is . . . .

Word Problem # 15

Read the word problem below.

15 children say they like to drink milk the best. 7 children like to drink juice.
How many more children like milk?

Write the equation , Show your work and solve it.

Your Answer is . . . .

Word Problem # 16

Read the word problem below.

There are 8 girls who have pets and 20 boys who have pets. How many more boys have pets than the girls?

Write the equation , Show your work and solve it.

Your Answer is . . . .

Word Problem # 17

Read the word problem below.

Jack has 13 stickers. Chris has fewer than Jack, but more than 11 stickers. How many stickers does Chris have?

Write the equation , Show your work and solve it.

Your Answer is . . . .

Word Problem # 18

Read the word problem below.

Jessy has 25 bracelets. She gives 20 to her sister. Then she gets 10 more for her birthday. How many bracelets does she have now?

Write the equation , Show your work and solve it.

Your Answer is . . . .

Word Problem # 19

Read the word problem below.

Ian has 10 red buttons and 3 blue buttons in a bag. What color button will he be more likely to pick from the bag? Why?

Write the equation , Show your work and solve it.

Your Answer is . . . .

Word Problem # 20

Read the word problem below.

The clown is holding 8 black balloons, 10 blue balloons, and 2 yellow balloons. How many balloons does he have?

Write the equation , Show your work and solve it.

Your Answer is . . . .

Word Problem # 21

Read the word problem below.

Ariana has 2 boxes of 10 pencils. She finds 1 more box of 10 pencils. How many pencils does she have now?

Write the equation , Show your work and solve it.

Your Answer is . . . .

Word Problem # 22

Read the word problem below.

There are 3 shelves. There are 10 books on each shelf. How many books are there in all? How many will be left if you take 5 away?

Write the equation , Show your work and solve it.

Your Answer is . . . .

Word Problem # 23

Read the word problem below.

Taylor counts her stickers. She puts them in 3 groups of ten and has 3 left over. How many stickers does she have?

Write the equation , Show your work and solve it.

Your Answer is . . . .

Word Problem # 24

Read the word problem below.

Frey got $27 as a gift. She got the money in tens and ones. How many tens and how many ones did she get?

Write the equation , Show your work and solve it.

Your Answer is . . . .

Word Problem # 25

Read the word problem below.

Boy has 50 markers. He wants to put them into boxes that hold 10 markers each. How many boxes does he need?

Write the equation , Show your work and solve it.

Your Answer is . . . .

Word Problem # 26

Read the word problem below.

There were 10 cars in the parking lot at 12:00pm. At 3:00pm, there were 7 more cars in the parking lot. How many cars in all were in the parking lot at 3:00pm?

Write the equation , Show your work and solve it.

Your Answer is . . . .

Word Problem # 27

Read the word problem below.

Last year, 30 stores opened for business at the outlet mall. Due to low sales, 5 of the stores closed down. How many stores are open for business at the outlet mall now?

Write the equation , Show your work and solve it.

Your Answer is . . . .

Word Problem # 28

Read the word problem below.

Alexa walks 11 blocks to school. Julia walks 20 blocks to school. Who has the longer walk? How many more blocks does she walk?

Write the equation , Show your work and solve it.

Your Answer is . . . .

Word Problem # 29

Read the word problem below.

Ava has 16 shells. Chad has 2 more shells than Ava. How many shells do they have in all?

Write the equation , Show your work and solve it.

Your Answer is . . . .

Word Problem # 30

Read the word problem below.

There are 17 cows at the farm. 10 cows are in the barn and some are in the field. How many cows are in the field?

Write the equation , Show your work and solve it.

Your Answer is . . . .

Word Problem # 31

Read the word problem below.

There are 22 apples on the tree. Kylie picked 3 apples and Zoey picked 6 apples. How many apples are left on the tree?

Write the equation , Show your work and solve it.

Your Answer is . . . .

Word Problem # 32

Read the word problem below.

Kevin has 18 pennies. He spends 5 pennies. Does he have enough left to buy a toy car for 12 pennies? If so, how much will he have left?

Write the equation , Show your work and solve it.

Your Answer is . . . .

Word Problem # 33

Read the word problem below.

Audrey has 15 stickers in her collection.
Tina has 3 fewer stickers.
How many stickers does Tina have?

Write the equation , Show your work and solve it.

Your Answer is . . . .

Word Problem # 34

Read the word problem below.

Leo collects 20 baseball cards. He gets 8 more from a friend. Then Eric gives 5 cards to Carter. How many cards does he have left?

Write the equation , Show your work and solve it.

Your Answer is . . . .

Word Problem # 35

Read the word problem below.

David is 8 years older than Liz. Nora is twice as old as Liz. Liz is 7 years old. How old is David and Nora? Show your work.

Write the equation , Show your work and solve it.

Your Answer is . . . .

Word Problem # 36

Read the word problem below.

Dylan drew 22 animals for his project. Then he drew 22 more animals. How many animals did Dylan draw for his project?

Write the equation , Show your work and solve it.

Your Answer is . . . .

Word Problem # 37

Read the word problem below.

Aiden drove his truck for 30 miles.
Sherry drove her truck 20 miles
further than Aiden.
How many miles did Sherry drive?

Write the equation , Show your work and solve it.

Your Answer is . . . .

Word Problem # 38

Read the word problem below.

Harper has 38 books. The shelves in her room hold 10 books each. How many shelves can she fill with books? How many books are left over?

Write the equation , Show your work and solve it.

Your Answer is . . . .

Word Problem # 39

Read the word problem below.

Chase has 6 more beads than Ethan. Anna has twice as many beads as Ethan. Ethan has 5 beads. How many beads do Chase and Anna have?

Write the equation , Show your work and solve it.

Your Answer is . . . .

Word Problem # 40

Read the word problem below.

Bailey makes 30 muffins for the bake sale. She sells half of them. How many muffins does she have left?

Write the equation , Show your work and solve it.

Your Answer is . . . .

Word Problem # 41

Read the word problem below.

What is this odd number: it is greater than 75 but less than 85. It has a 3 in the ones place. What number is it?

Write the equation , Show your work and solve it.

Your Answer is . . . .

Word Problem # 42

Read the word problem below.

Pencils come in boxes of 12, 18, and 24. Mr. Patt wants to buy 30 pencils. Which two boxes should she buy?

Write the equation , Show your work and solve it.

Your Answer is . . . .

Word Problem # 43

Read the word problem below.

Bobby collected 15 rocks. Dan collected 23 rocks. How many rocks did they collect in all?

Write the equation , Show your work and solve it.

Your Answer is . . . .

Word Problem # 44

Read the word problem below.

Brooke has 70 stickers. She gives Tracy 40 stickers. How many stickers does Brooke have now?

Write the equation , Show your work and solve it.

Your Answer is . . . .

Word Problem # 45

Read the word problem below.

Nicky burned 20 more calories than Kayla walking up a hill. Nicky burned 50 calories. How many calories did Kayla burn?

Write the equation , Show your work and solve it.

Your Answer is . . . .

Word Problem # 46

Read the word problem below.

Sully has 7 more toys than Bella. Sully has 58 toys. How many toys does Bella have?

Write the equation , Show your work and solve it.

Your Answer is . . . .

Word Problem # 47

Read the word problem below.

Rosie has basketball practice 3 days each week. How many days does she not have practice each week?

Write the equation , Show your work and solve it.

Your Answer is . . . .

Word Problem # 48

Read the word problem below.

Micheal has 13 more pennies than Lucas does. Lucas has 52 pennies. How may pennies does Micheal have?

Write the equation , Show your work and solve it.

Your Answer is . . . .

Word Problem # 49

Read the word problem below.

Jody has 9 tickets and she uses 2 of them. Frank has 12 tickets and uses 6 of them. How many total tickets do they have left?

Write the equation , Show your work and solve it.

Your Answer is . . . .

Word Problem # 50

Read the word problem below.

Lanna had 17 erasers. She got 9 more. Later she gave 7 of the erasers to her brother. How many does she have now?

Write the equation , Show your work and solve it.

Your Answer is . . . .

Word Problem # 51

Read the word problem below.

Olsen brings 7 balls and 3 cars to the park.
Eve brings 6 balls and 4 cars.
Which child brings more toys?

Write the equation , Show your work and solve it.

Your Answer is . . . .

Word Problem # 52

Read the word problem below.

The class has 20 pencils. Shelby uses 4 pencils and Finn brings in 17 more. How many pencils does the class have now?

Write the equation , Show your work and solve it.

Your Answer is . . . .

Word Problem # 53

Read the word problem below.

Eden has 55 coins. A friends gives her 8 more coins. How many coins does Eden have now?

Write the equation , Show your work and solve it.

Your Answer is . . . .

Word Problem # 54

Read the word problem below.

Chris has a collection of 61 football cards. He buys 39 more cards. How many football cards does he have now?

Write the equation , Show your work and solve it.

Your Answer is . . . .

Word Problem # 55

Read the word problem below.

Drake has 35 marbles and finds 18 more. Jessie has 25 marbles and finds 15 more. Who has more marbles?

Write the equation , Show your work and solve it.

Your Answer is . . . .

Word Problem # 56

Read the word problem below.

Mr. Dough sells colored pencils. He sells 59 green, 34 blue, and 41 yellow pencils. How many more green pencils did he sell than blue?

Write the equation , Show your work and solve it.

Your Answer is . . . .

Word Problem # 57

Read the word problem below.

Harry found 44 rocks
for his collection.
His sister gave him 16 more.
How many rocks does he have now?

Write the equation , Show your work and solve it.

Your Answer is . . . .

Word Problem # 58

Read the word problem below.

A bus with 30 people on it stops at Dock St. Ten people get off, and 3 get on. At Barr St. 5 people get off, and 7 get on. How many people are on the bus?

Write the equation , Show your work and solve it.

Your Answer is . . . .

Word Problem # 59

Read the word problem below.

There are 71 birds. 40 of the birds are robins. The rest of the birds are bluebirds. How many bluebirds are there?

Write the equation , Show your work and solve it.

Your Answer is . . . .

Word Problem # 60

Read the word problem below.

There are 64 chickens on the farm. 48 of the chickens are white and the rest are black How many chickens are black?

Write the equation , Show your work and solve it.

Your Answer is . . . .

Word Problem # 61

Read the word problem below.

Lydia sold 25 large balls and 13 small balls. Molly sold 14 large balls and 19 small balls. Who sold more balls? How many more?

Write the equation , Show your work and solve it.

Your Answer is . . . .

Word Problem # 62

Read the word problem below.

There are 60 animals at the farm. 25 of the animals are horses and the rest are chickens. How many chickens are at the farm?

Write the equation , Show your work and solve it.

Your Answer is . . . .

Word Problem # 63

Read the word problem below.

At 5:00 pm there were 21 kids playing on the playground. Thirty minutes later, 2 more kids showed up to play. At 6:05 pm, 14 kids left the playground to go home. How many kids were still playing on the playground?

Write the equation , Show your work and solve it.

Your Answer is . . . .

Word Problem # 64

Read the word problem below.

There are many different sized houses in my neighborhood. My house has 7 rooms. My neighbor's house has 13 rooms. How many fewer rooms does my house have than my neighbors do?

Write the equation , Show your work and solve it.

Your Answer is . . . .

Word Problem # 65

Read the word problem below.

Elza was supposed to meet Anna at the library at 4:30. Anna was 17 minutes late. What time did Anna get to the library?

Write the equation , Show your work and solve it.

Your Answer is . . . .

Word Problem # 66

Read the word problem below.

Taissa plays soccer every Saturday. If this Saturday is the 10th, what date will next Saturday be?

Write the equation , Show your work and solve it.

Your Answer is . . . .

Word Problem # 67

Read the word problem below.

Tim's lunchbox is 15 inches long.
Lola's lunchbox is 12 inches long.
Whose lunchbox is longer? How much longer?

Write the equation , Show your work and solve it.

Your Answer is . . . .

Word Problem # 68

Read the word problem below.

Eric makes a square wooden frame to put around a picture. One side measures 8 inches. How many inches of wood does Eric use in all?

Write the equation , Show your work and solve it.

Your Answer is . . . .

Word Problem # 69

Read the word problem below.

A box of apples weighs 30 pounds.
Ali took 10 pounds of apples out.
Then he put 15 pounds of apples in.
How much does the box weightnow?

Write the equation , Show your work and solve it.

Your Answer is . . . .

Word Problem # 70

Read the word problem below.

Kimberly uses 8 cups of orange juice and 67 cups of apple juice. How many more cups of apple juice does Kimberly use?

Write the equation , Show your work and solve it.

Your Answer is . . . .

Word Problem # 71

Read the word problem below.

Tyler has two quarters in his pocket. How many nickels would he need to have the same amount of money as two quarters?

Write the equation, Show your work and solve it.

Your Answer is . . . .

Word Problem # 72

Read the word problem below.

The school store is having a sale. All pencils are 10 cents. A child bought 4 green pencils and 3 blue pencils. What was the total cost of the pencils?

Write the equation , Show your work and solve it.

Your Answer is . . . .

Word Problem # 73

Read the word problem below.

The baker bakes 99 loaves of bread. He sells 43 loaves. How many loaves of bread are left?

Write the equation , Show your work and solve it.

Your Answer is . . . .

Word Problem # 74

Read the word problem below.

Blake finds 24 orange leaves and some yellow leaves. He finds 42 leaves in all. How many yellow leaves does he find?

Write the equation , Show your work and solve it.

Your Answer is . . . .

Word Problem # 75

Read the word problem below.

Mr. Stone sells cars. He wants to sell 110 cars this month. So far he has sold 67 cars. How many more cars does he need to sell?

Write the equation , Show your work and solve it.

Your Answer is . . . .

Word Problem # 76

Read the word problem below.

Aaron made 25 fewer shots than Adam did in the basketball game. Adam made 43 shots. How many shots did Arron make?

Write the equation , Show your work and solve it.

Your Answer is . . . .

Word Problem # 77

Read the word problem below.

Jasmine counted 41 can goods in her mother's pantry. Her mother went shopping and added more cans to the pantry. There are now 49 can goods in the pantry. How many cans did jasmine's mother add to the pantry?

Write the equation , Show your work and solve it.

Your Answer is . . . .

Word Problem # 78

Read the word problem below.

Payton counted 29 red cars on the way to soccer practice. He counted 7 fewer red cars on the way home from soccer practice. How many cars did Payton count on the way

Write the equation , Show your work and solve it.

Your Answer is . . . .

Word Problem # 79

Read the word problem below.

Tony has 89 dollars. Darah has 40 dollars. How many more dollars does Tony have than Darah?

Write the equation , Show your work and solve it.

Your Answer is . . . .

Word Problem # 80

Read the word problem below.

Yesterday, at the book fair, Jason bought 21 purple mechanical pencils. Today, he bought 10 red mechanical pencils. How many mechanical pencils did he buy in all?

Write the equation , Show your work and solve it.

Your Answer is . . . .

Answer Key

1. 40
2. 12
3. 4 more
4. Leia has 5 less
5. 4
6. 5 left
7. 4 in front and 4 in bqck
8. 14 sides
9. 0 penny
10. Greg
11. 14
12. 6
13. 16 people
14. 8 stamps
15. 8 more
16. 12
17. 12
18. 15
19. red
20. 20
21. 30
22. 30,25
23. 33
24. 2 tens 7 ones
25. 5 boxes
26. 17
27. 25
28. Julia , 9 more
29. 18+16 =34
30. 7
31. 13
32. Yes , 1 penny left
33. 12
34. 23
35. David 15 , Nora 14
36. 44
37. 50
38. 3 shelves , 8 left
39. Chase 11 , Anna 10
40. 15 left
41. 83
42. 12 and 18
43. 38 rocks
44. 30 stickers
45. 30 calories
46. 51
47. 4 days
48. 65 pennies
49. 13 tickets
50. 19 erasers

Answer Key

51. they bring same amount of toy
52. 33 pencils
53. 63 coins
54. 100 cards
55. Drake has more
56. 25 more
57. 69 rocks
58. 25 people
59. 31
60. 16
61. Lydia , 5 more
62. 35 chickens
63. 9 kids.
64. 6 rooms
65. 4.47
66. 17th
67. Tim's, 3inches
68. 32 inches
69. 35 pounds
70. 59 cups.
71. 10 nickels
72. 70 cents
73. 56 loaves
74. 18
75. 43 cars
76. 18 shots
77. 8 cans
78. 51 cans
79. 49 dollars
80. 31 pencils

Made in United States
North Haven, CT
22 April 2022

18467591R00050